To:

_____

From:

_____

Date:

_____

Published by Christian Art Publishers
PO Box 1599, Vereeniging, 1930, RSA

© 2016
First edition 2016

Designed by Christian Art Publishers

Images used under license from Shutterstock.com

Printed in China

ISBN 978-1-4321-1688-0 CLR024
ISBN 978-1-64272-761-6 CLR064
ISBN 978-1-64272-763-0 CLR066
ISBN 978-1-64272-906-1 XCLR077

21 22 23 24 25 26 27 28 29 30 – 24 23 22 21 20 19 18 17 16 15

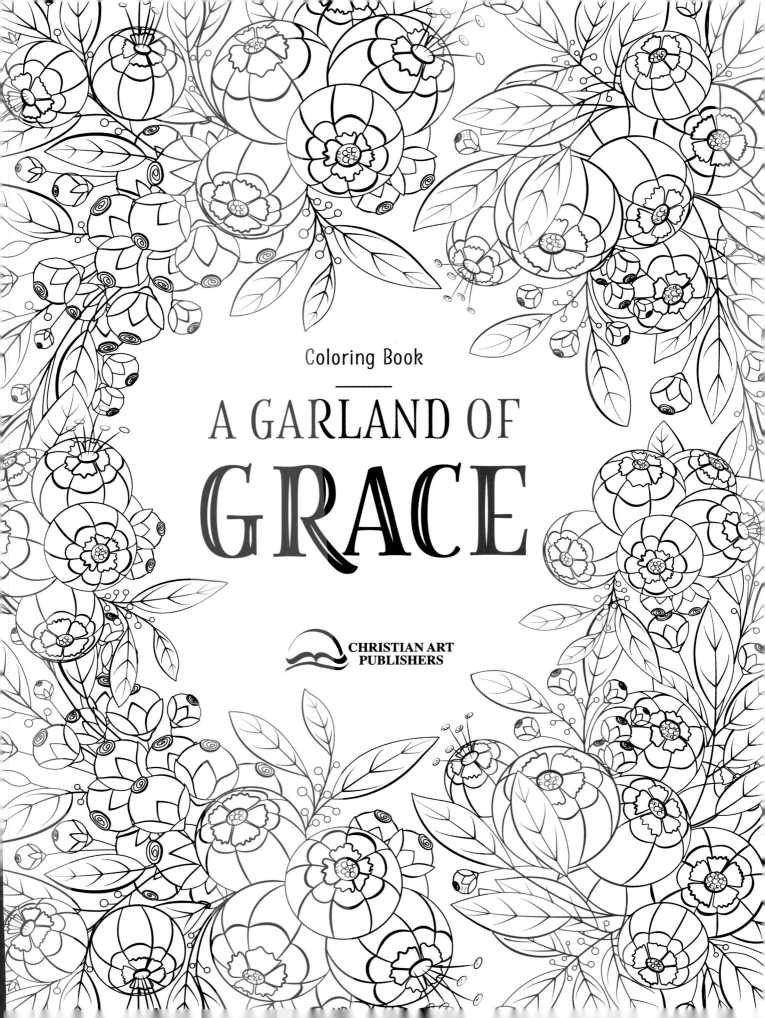

Coloring Book

A GARLAND OF
GRACE

**CHRISTIAN ART
PUBLISHERS**

WISDOM
will give you a
garland
to grace
your head
and present you with a
glorious
crown.
Proverbs 4:9

By *wisdom* a house is built, and through **understanding** it is established; through *knowledge* its rooms are filled with rare and beautiful *treasures.*

Proverbs 24:3-4

The path of the righteous is like the morning sun, shining ever brighter till the full light of day.

Proverbs 4:18

ABOVE ALL ELSE,
GUARD YOUR *heart,*
FOR EVERYTHING
YOU DO FLOWS
FROM IT.

PROVERBS 4:23

Never let
loyalty &
kindness
leave you!
Tie them around your
neck as a reminder.
Write them deep within
your heart.
Proverbs 3:3

She is clothed with strength & dignity, and she laughs without fear of the future.

Proverbs 31:25

Gracious words are a HONEYCOMB, SWEET TO THE soul & healing to the bones. Proverbs 16:24

Charm is deceptive, and beauty is fleeting; but a woman who fears the *Lord* is to be *praised.*

Proverbs 31:30

The
blessing
of the Lord
makes
a person rich,
and He adds
no sorrow
with it.
Proverbs 10:22

A gentle answer deflects anger, but harsh words make tempers flare.

Proverbs 15:1

Fear of the **Lord** is the foundation of WISDOM. Knowledge of the *Holy One* results in good judgment.

Proverbs 9:10

Love covers over all wrongs.

Proverbs 10:12

Those who listen to instruction will prosper; those who trust the Lord will be joyful.

Proverbs 16:20

TRUST in the Lord with all your HEART & lean not on your own understanding; in all your ways submit to Him, & He will make your PATHS straight.

Proverbs 3:5-6

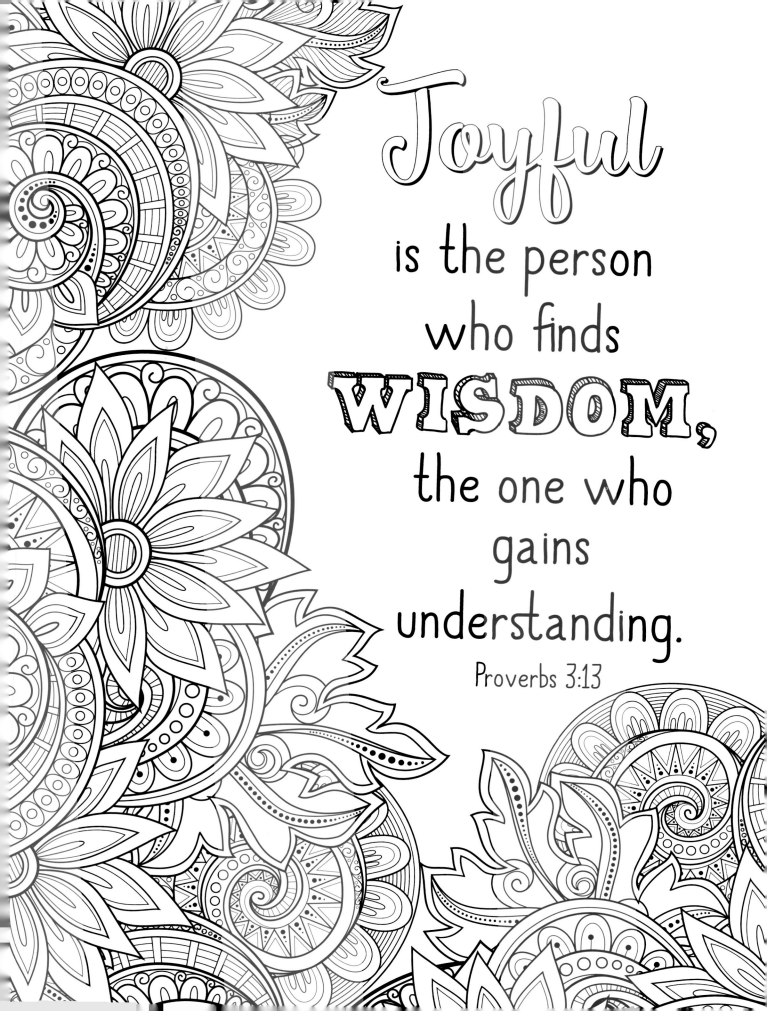

Joyful is the person who finds WISDOM, the one who gains understanding.

Proverbs 3:13

HER
CHILDREN ARISE
& call her
blessed;
HER HUSBAND ALSO,
& he praises her:
"MANY WOMEN DO
noble Things,
BUT YOU SURPASS
THEM ALL."

Proverbs 31:28-29

Worry weighs a person down;
an encouraging word
cheers a person up.

Proverbs 12:25

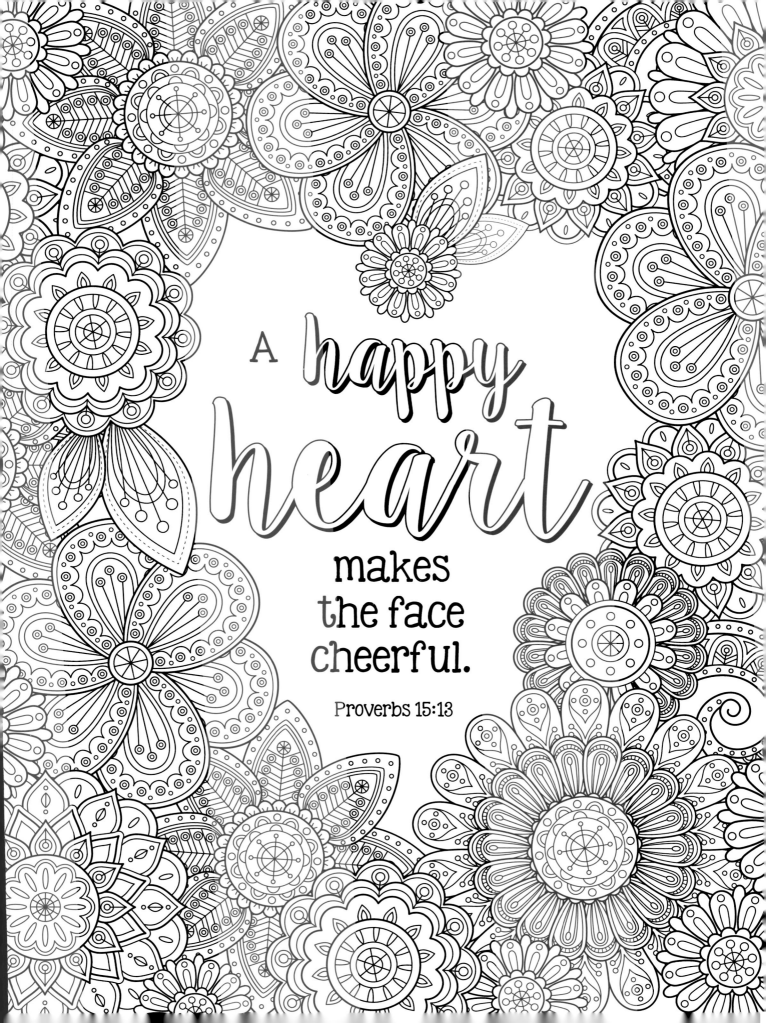

A *happy* **heart** makes the face cheerful.

Proverbs 15:13

A real *friend* sticks closer than a *brother.*

Proverbs 18:24

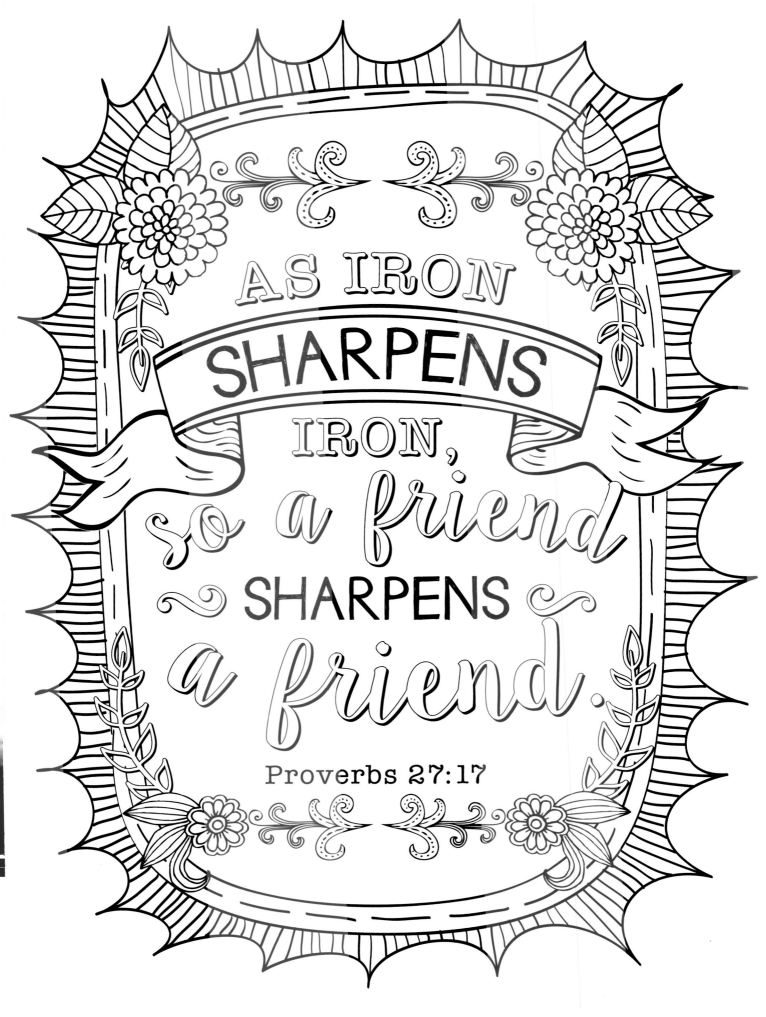

The name of the Lord is a strong fortress; the godly run to Him and are safe. Proverbs 18:10

Start children off on the way they should go, and even when they are old they will not turn from it.

Proverbs 22:6

FEAR OF THE LORD IS THE FOUNDATION OF TRUE KNOWLEDGE

Proverbs 1:7

Honor the *Lord* with your wealth, with the firstfruits of all your crops.

Proverbs 3:9

WALK WITH
THE WISE AND BECOME
wise,
FOR A COMPANION OF FOOLS
SUFFERS HARM.

PROVERBS 13:20

The highway of the upright avoids evil; those who guard their ways preserve their lives.

Proverbs 16:17

A gift opens the way and ushers the giver into the presence of the great.

Proverbs 18:16

Many are the plans in a person's **heart**, but it is the **Lord's** purpose that prevails.

Proverbs 19:21

Better to have little,
with fear for the Lord,
than to have great
treasure and inner turmoil.

Proverbs 15:16

DO NOT FORSAKE *wisdom*, AND SHE WILL PROTECT YOU; *love* HER, & SHE WILL WATCH OVER YOU.

PROVERBS 4:6

A gossip goes around telling secrets,
but those who are trustworthy
can keep a confidence.

Proverbs 11:13

WISE

words bring many benefits,
and hard work brings rewards.

Proverbs 12:14

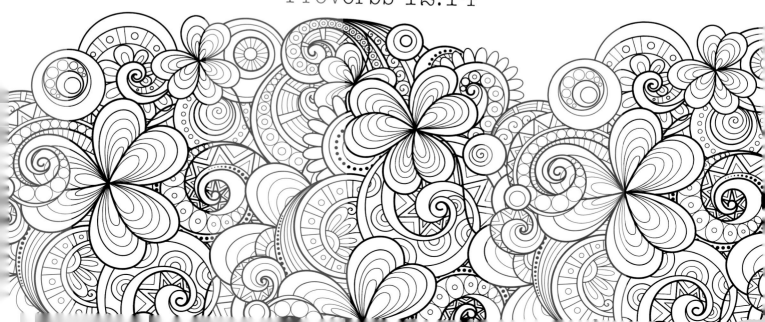

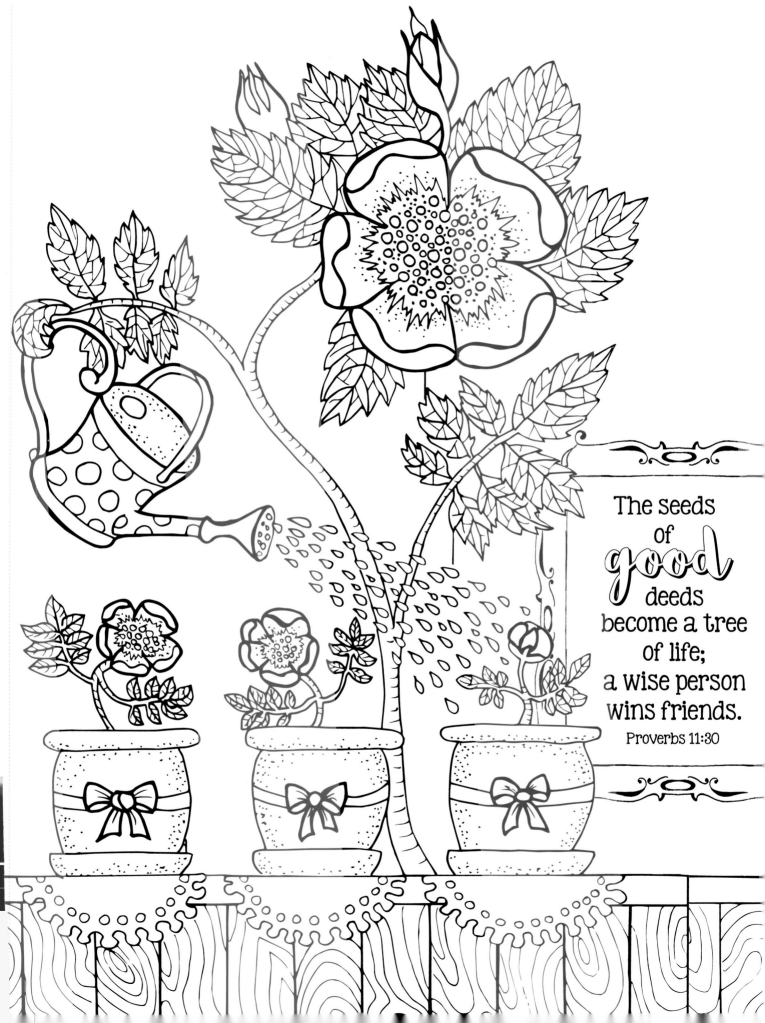

The seeds
of
good
deeds
become a tree
of life;
a wise person
wins friends.

Proverbs 11:30

For the LORD will be at your side and will keep your foot from being snared.

Proverbs 3:26

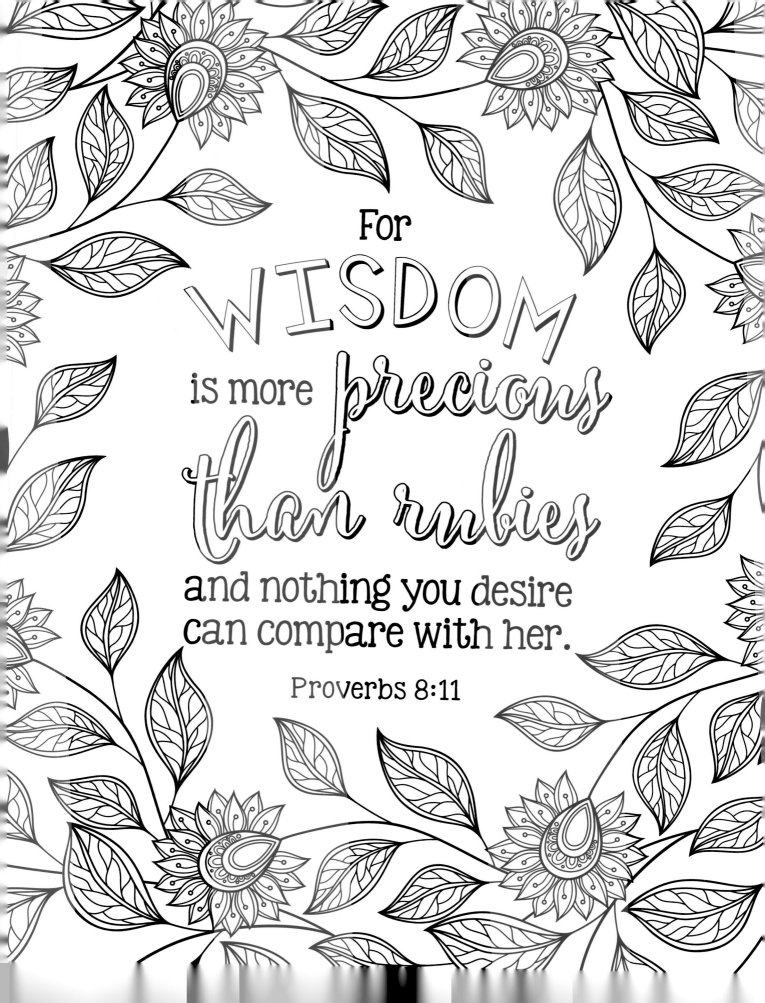

For the **Lord** corrects those He **LOVES,** just as a father corrects a child in whom he delights.

Proverbs 3:12

In the way of righteousness there is *life;* along that path is immortality.

Proverbs 12:28

Whoever *fears* the LORD has a secure fortress, and for their children it will be a *refuge.*

Proverbs 14:26

HE GUARDS THE *paths* OF THE JUST AND PROTECTS THOSE WHO ARE *faithful* TO *Him.*

PROVERBS 2:8

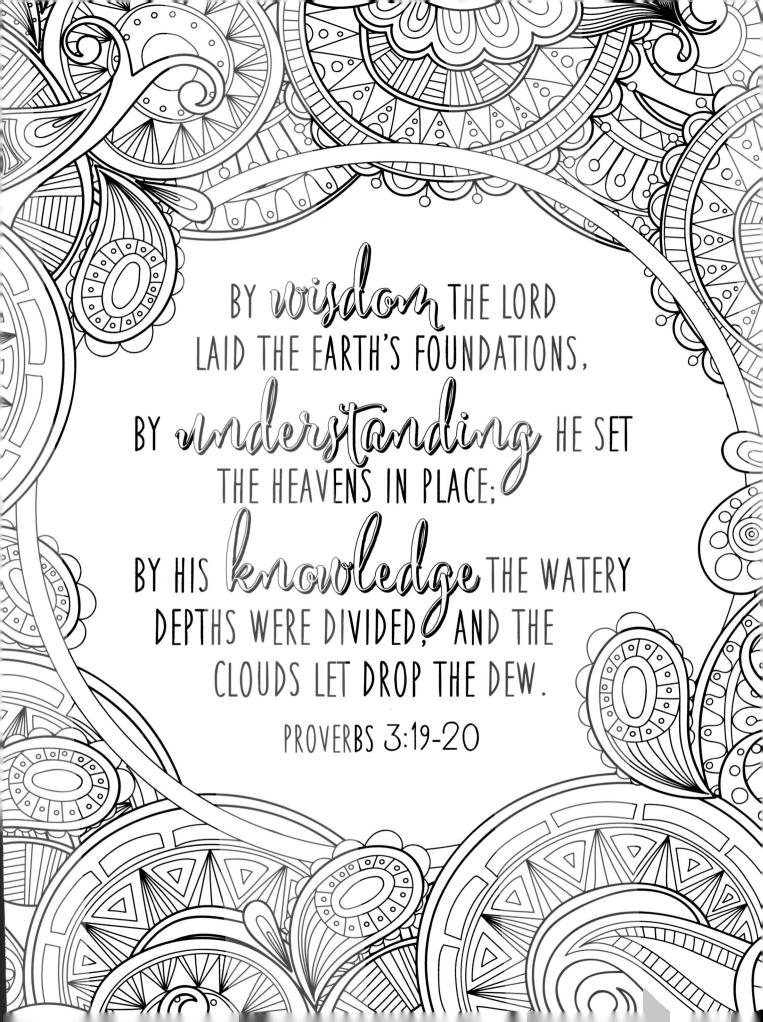

BY *wisdom* THE LORD
LAID THE EARTH'S FOUNDATIONS,
BY *understanding* HE SET
THE HEAVENS IN PLACE;
BY HIS *knowledge* THE WATERY
DEPTHS WERE DIVIDED, AND THE
CLOUDS LET DROP THE DEW.
PROVERBS 3:19-20

When the storm has swept by, the wicked are gone, but the *righteous* stand firm forever.
Proverbs 10:25

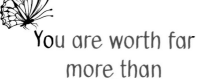
You are worth far more than

rubies !

Proverbs 31:10

Good planning & hard work lead to prosperity.

Proverbs 21:5

Kind words are like honey — sweet to the soul and healthy for the body.

Proverbs 16:24

The name of the Lord is a strong fortress; the godly run to Him and are safe.

Proverbs 18:10

The
heartfelt
counsel of a friend is
as sweet as
perfume and incense.

Proverbs 27:9

Whoever
fears
the LORD has
a secure fortress,
and for their
children it will be a
refuge.

Proverbs 14:26

Many are the
plans in a
person's
heart,
but it is
the
Lord's
purpose
that prevails.

Proverbs 19:21

BY *wisdom* THE LORD
LAID THE EARTH'S FOUNDATIONS,
BY
understanding
HE SET THE HEAVENS IN PLACE;
BY HIS
knowledge THE WATERY
DEPTHS WERE DIVIDED, AND
THE CLOUDS LET DROP THE DEW.

PROVERBS 3:19-20

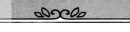

FOLD

A woman who fears the *Lord* is to be *praised.*

Proverbs 31:30

Proverbs 31:10

You are worth far more than rubies!

Those who trust in the Lord will be joyful.

Proverbs 16:20

FOLD

TRUST in the Lord with all your HEART.

Proverbs 3:5

Commit your actions to the Lord, and your plans will succeed.

Proverbs 16:3

Quiz Number	Question Number	Answer	Core Concept Reference
21	1.	d) 22	CC 38
	2.	d) 96	CC 59
	3.	a) 288 cu. ft.	CC 56
	4.	c) 435	CC 48
	5.	b) 1,260	CC 60
22	1.	b) 8°	CC 64
	2.	d) $x = 10$	CC 74
	3.	b) $y = 4x + 13$	CC 69
	4.	b) 17	CC 6
	5.	a) 54.5	CC 19
23	1.	c) 9	CC 74
	2.	c) 72	CC 67
	3.	a) 83.3	CC 81
	4.	c) 6	CC 8
	5.	d) $3,650	CC 41
24	1.	d) $\frac{4}{7}$	CC 13
	2.	a) it is translated 4 units vertically up	CC 75
	3.	b) 86.4 miles	CC 47
	4.	a) $(4x - 5y)(4x + 5y)$	CC 37
	5.	c) $6x^8$	CC 29
25	1.	a) 4	CC 15
	2.	d) 35	CC 17
	3.	b) 2π	CC 52
	4.	a) $y = 3^x$	CC 29
	5.	b) $\frac{1}{25}$	CC 23

Made in United States
Orlando, FL
16 May 2022

17924637R00320